LEARNING TO LIVE SERIES

DISCIPLINES OF LIVING

NAVPRESS
A MINISTRY OF THE NAVIGATORS
P.O. Box 6000, Colorado Springs, Colorado 80934

The Navigators is an international Christian organization. Jesus Christ gave His followers the Great Commission to go and make disciples (Matthew 28:19). The aim of The Navigators is to help fulfill that commission by multiplying laborers for Christ in every nation.

NavPress is the publishing ministry of The Navigators. NavPress publications are tools to help Christians grow. Although publications alone cannot make disciples or change lives, they can help believers learn biblical discipleship, and apply what they learn to their lives and ministries.

© 1987 The Navigators Great Britain
All rights reserved, including translation
ISBN: 0-89109-059-2
10595

Printed in the United States of America

Contents

Author

The LEARNING TO LIVE series was written by Peter Dowse. Born in Great Britain, he has degrees from Cambridge University and London Bible College. Peter has been on staff with The Navigators since 1977. He led the student ministry at Sheffield University for several years, and now gives his time to writing and speaking.

Make the Most of This Bible Study

We live in a world of shifting values and conflicting viewpoints. Is it possible in the midst of this to know what is right and what is true? Yes it is! For God is true, and He has chosen to give us in the Bible a definitive expression of His own mind and will, His knowledge of reality, and His thoughts and plans for the world.

> *You will know the truth,*
> *and the truth will set you free.*
> (JOHN 8:32)

It is the aim of this Bible study series to introduce you to the joy and privilege of digging out that truth for yourself.

Personal Bible study is demanding. You will need to give it much time and serious endeavor. In this series, each lesson takes two to three hours to prepare. The rewards of personal Bible study, however, are great. You will surely discover this for yourself as you complete the books in this series.

Remember that Bible study is not merely an academic exercise. You will need to think, but don't forget that the Bible is God's Word. Pray before you start each lesson. Ask God to help you understand the truths and make you sensitive to what He wants to say to you through a particular lesson. Pray as you study, "Lord, what does this mean? How does this relate to me?" Praise Him when you discover something that excites you. The fruit of Bible study should not be just increased head knowledge; it should produce a deeper relationship with God and a lifestyle that is more honoring to Him.

If you can find others who are willing to put in the time to do personal preparation, you will find great value in meeting together to discuss each lesson. But don't let the absence of such a group deter you. Get into God's Word for yourself. You won't be disappointed.

> *When your words came, I ate them;*
> *they were my joy and my heart's delight.*
> (JEREMIAH 15:16)

SOME EXPLANATIONS: The definitions given throughout this series are, of necessity, brief. More exhaustive definitions of the words can be found in any good Bible dictionary, for example, *The Illustrated Bible Dictionary*, published by Inter-Varsity Press.

Whenever the name of a person who has been quoted is followed by an asterisk, you will find information about that person in "Who's Who" on page 91.

Additional references are listed for some questions. They are optional references that you can use if you want to. For an example, see question 3 on pages 27 and 28.

Each lesson has sections entitled "Ask Yourself." These do not require written responses, though you may want to write answers to the questions in a notebook. Each lesson also has a section entitled "For Further Study." These sections are optional.

The six books in the *Learning to Live* series can be done in any order, or you can follow this suggested sequence:

Clarifying Your Commitment
Living by His Grace
Living in the World
Disciplines of Living
Your Part in His Plan
Standing Firm

Pleasing to God

As growing Christians, we are developing a very different perspective on life. God as revealed in Jesus Christ is now our ultimate reference point. We want to know His values and standards. We want to please Him.

This desire needs to grow and develop. In this book, we will take a closer look at what God is like—His holiness, His greatness and goodness, His wisdom and power, His love and sovereignty. And we will make some decisions about how He wants us to respond practically to these aspects of His character.

Our perspective on the Christian life is broadening and becoming more biblical. There *is* joy in living for God, but it is the mature joy of a deeply satisfying relationship, not a shallow happiness that ignores the harsh realities of life.

Holiness

Holiness is not a popular word, even in many Christian circles. One reason may be the misconceptions people have about the meaning of the word. To some, it suggests the smug self-righteousness of the Pharisee with his endless list of dos and don'ts. Other people think of those who, in the name of religion, isolate themselves as far as possible from contact with the sinful world. Still others may view holiness as something for special people—the "saints"—but unattainable for ordinary people living ordinary lives.

The Bible delivers us from such misconceptions. God Himself is holy, and we will begin the lesson by examining what that means. It is an awe-inspiring truth and also a powerful incentive to discover what it means for us to be His holy people. The second half of the lesson concentrates on how to pursue holiness in our own lives.

HOLY: The word that is translated "holy" and the similar words that are translated "sanctify" and "saint" have the root meaning of "separated" or "set apart" in the original Hebrew.

Pause for Prayer

In Luke 10:38-42, Jesus commended Mary because she didn't allow herself to be distracted by other pressing needs, but sat at His feet and listened to His teaching. Pause now and ask God to give you that same attitude of devoted attention and humble submission.

The Holy God

In this section, we will focus on Isaiah's vision of God, recorded in Isaiah 6:1-8. Read these verses, and then consider parts of the passage as you answer the questions below. Ask God to help you share the reality of Isaiah's vision.

Awesome and Supreme

> Who among the gods is like you, O Lord?
> Who is like you—
> majestic in holiness,
> awesome in glory,
> working wonders?
> (Exodus 15:11)

---

1. What do you notice about God in Isaiah 6:1-4?

---

2. How do the following references compare with Isaiah's vision of God?

   Exodus 19:16-22

2 Samuel 6:1-7 (Also see Numbers 4:15.)

Mark 9:2-7

Pure and Righteous

God is infinitely superior to all other beings. He is on another plane. He is the Holy One. But there is more to God's holiness; He is also pure and righteous.

> *Your eyes are too pure to look on evil;*
> *you cannot tolerate wrong.*
> (Habbakuk 1:13)

---

3. How did Isaiah react to God's holiness? Read Isaiah 6:5.

---

4. What do the following statements teach about the holiness of God?

Psalm 5:4-6

Nahum 1:2-8

Romans 1:18, 2:5-11

"The wrath of God is a perfection of the Divine character on which we need to meditate frequently. First, that our hearts may be duly impressed by God's detestation of sin. . . . Second, to beget a true fear in our souls for God. . . . Third, to draw out our soul in fervent praise to Jesus Christ for having delivered us from 'the wrath to come.'"[1] —A.W. PINK

Just and Merciful

He is the Rock, his works are perfect,
and all his ways are just.
A faithful God who does no wrong,
upright and just is he.
(Deuteronomy 32:4)

---

5. Read Isaiah 6:6-8.

   a. In what ways does Isaiah's experience point forward to the work of Christ?

b. According to Romans 3:21-26, how does the work of Christ make it possible for God to be both just and merciful?

c. What effect did God's mercy have on Isaiah?

Because God is so different from us, He takes the initiative to show mercy to the undeserving (see Hosea 11:8-9). But because He will not compromise His justice, He takes that initiative at great cost to Himself. It is a great mistake for us to focus on the mercy of God and to forget that it is a *holy* mercy. The God who forgives us and accepts us in Christ is still the awesome and supreme God with whom we must not trifle. He is still the pure and righteous God who hates sin and is implacably opposed to it.

The letter to the Hebrews brings this out. On the one hand, it gives a clear exposition of the way in which God has shown mercy to us in Christ. It stresses that through Christ we can now draw near to God with confidence and assurance (see Hebrews 10:19-22). On the other hand, however, there is the constant reminder that God is still the same Holy God who was revealed in Old Testament days.

---

6. Read Hebrews 12:14-29.

a. What contrasts do you see between the Christian attitude toward God and the attitude of the people of

13

Israel when they received the Ten Commandments (see Exodus 20:18-21)?

b. What should our response to God be?

"In olden days men of faith were said to 'walk in the fear of God' and to 'serve the Lord with fear.' However intimate their communion with God, however bold their prayers, at the base of their religious life was the conception of God as awesome and dreadful. . . . The self-assurance of modern Christians, the basic levity present in so many of our religious gatherings, the shocking disrespect shown for the Person of God, are evidences enough of deep blindness of heart."[2] — A.W. TOZER

Holiness Means Separation

The holiness of God means, first of all, that He is separate from all other beings. He is infinitely above them. He alone is God. As the hymnwriter puts it, "Only Thou art holy, there is none beside Thee." Second, He is separate from any flaw or limitation in His purity. He is the absolute standard of morality, and He always acts in a way that is entirely consistent with that standard. Third, God's holiness means that He responds actively against all unrighteousness and, in judgment, separates Himself from all that opposes His will or contradicts His nature.

"Fred, I think you're taking this holiness thing too far!"

A Holy People

Our great God and Savior, Jesus Christ . . . gave himself for us to redeem us from all wickedness and to purify for himself a people that are his very own, eager to do what is good.
(Titus 2:13-14)

The word *holy* is used in two ways with regard to Christians. First, it describes our *position* before God, our *settled relationship* with Him. We become holy in this way the moment we become Christians because our sins are forgiven and we are adopted into the family of God. Hence, the New Testament frequently refers to Christians as "the saints." However, our position should not be confused with our *condition*. As far as our character is concerned, there is need for increasing holiness, a *progressive renewal* in the image of Christ.

These two dimensions of holiness are linked because an appreciation of our position acts as a powerful incentive to change our condition. This is clearly seen in the passage we will focus on in the second half of this lesson. Read 1 Peter 1:13-2:12 to get an overview, and then consider the questions that follow.

---

7. a. Read verses 13-16 of 1 Peter 1 again. Why should we be holy?

b. List the actions we are commanded to take and explain what each one means.

16

> "Only as we accept our responsibility and appropriate God's provisions will we make any progress in our pursuit of holiness."[3]
>
> —JERRY BRIDGES

8. a. What does 1 Peter 1:17-21 teach about the attitude we should have toward God, and why?

   b. How would such an attitude affect the way we live?

> "No sin is little in itself, because it is a contradiction of the nature and majesty of God." —JOHN BUNYAN*

9. Read 1 Peter 1:22–2:3.

   a. The passage highlights the fact that we have been born again. What should be our response to this?

b. Read the section entitled "The New Birth." Then explain why 1 Peter 2:1 begins with the word *therefore*.

The New Birth

The Old Me: Because of the Fall, every human being is dominated by a sinful nature and is subject to death. Apart from Christ, death marks the ultimate triumph for sin and is a prelude to what the Bible calls the second death.

The New Me in the Making: When we become Christians, the Holy Spirit imparts to us a new spiritual life. We become new people, part of the new creation God began with Christ and will complete when He returns. However, we are not immediately removed from the old creation. We remain a part of it, continuing to live in a world corrupted by sin and Satan. Although the dominating power of our sinful nature is broken, we can still be pulled into sin by its powerful influence.

The New Me: Death and/or the return of Christ will finally free us from our sinful nature. Christ's return will spell the end for Satan and will result in the creation of a new Heaven and a new earth. At that point, God will provide us with new bodies adapted to our new life. We will be free to live sinless lives in a sinless environment.

Central to holy living now is the recognition that the impulses of the sinful nature really belong to an old way of life. The spiritual nature is "the real me," and every act of repentance and obedience is a move in the right direction, freeing us from the restrictions of sin. (For the biblical basis, see Romans 5-8.)

Natural body (mortal) — Sinful nature — **The Old Me**

New birth →

Natural body (mortal) — Old sinful / New spiritual nature (the Holy Spirit) / nature — **The New Me in the Making**

Death and/or Christ's return →

Spiritual body (immortal) — Spiritual nature — **The New Me**

---

10. According to Galatians 5:16, what is crucial if we are to obey the commands in 1 Peter 1:22-2:3? (This is developed in "For Further Study.")

---

11. Read 1 Peter 2:5-8. Verse 5 includes two descriptions that communicate a great deal about our privileged position as Christians, and the responsibility that goes with it. Prayerfully think about what these pictures reveal. Also refer to the cross-references.

   a. "Living stones . . . being built into a spiritual house"
      Cross-references: 1 Corinthians 3:16
                        Ephesians 2:19-22

   What does the picture reveal about our privileged position as Christians?

What is the place of Jesus Christ in making this possible?

What responsibility goes with the privilege?

b. "A holy priesthood, offering spiritual sacrifices"
   Cross-references: Romans 12:1
                     Hebrews 13:15-16

   What does the picture reveal about our privileged position as Christians?

   What is the place of Jesus Christ in making this possible?

   What responsibility goes with the privilege?

---

12. Look at 1 Peter 2:9-12.

   a. What further insight do you find about our privileged position as Christians?

b. How should our understanding of this affect our behavior?

c. In 2 Corinthians 11:2-3, the Apostle Paul stresses this same truth of the privilege and responsibility of belonging to God. What can you learn from the way he puts it?

"As it upsets a man more to learn that his wife is sleeping around than that the girl next door is doing it, so God is most deeply outraged when His own people are unfaithful."[4] —J.I. PACKER

Holiness means separation. We have been set apart by God for Himself; we are His people and must behave as though we belong to Him. In daily living we should separate ourselves from all that opposes God's will or contradicts His character.

ASK YOURSELF: a. How can I strengthen my motivation to grow in holiness? **b.** How can I more effectively deal with sin in my life?

For Further Study
Galatians 5:13-25 describes the battle for holiness that goes on in our lives. Even as Christians, we sometimes indulge the sinful

nature. The key to not doing so lies in the work of the Holy Spirit in our lives and our response to Him.

A. Look at verse 16.

Based on the following verses, what is involved in living by the Spirit?

Romans 8:5 and Galatians 5:17

Romans 8:13 and Galatians 5:24

What can you learn about practical steps you must take to live by the Spirit?

B. Look at verse 18.

What do you think it means to be "led by the Spirit"?

How could you more fully experience the leading of the Spirit?

C. Look at verse 25.

What do you think it means to "keep in step with the Spirit"? (The literal meaning is "walk along the path the Spirit lays down.")

What related ideas do you find in Galatians 6:7-9 and 1 Timothy 4:7-8?

D. Prayerfully respond to the following questions.

Is my attitude toward the Holy Spirit right? Am I continually opening up my life to Him? Am I following the guidance He gives me in Scripture? Do I respond to His daily reminders of how I should live?

Is my attitude toward my sinful nature right? Do I really want to be changed? Am I committed to putting sinful attitudes to death, or do I just want to prevent the worst sinful actions?

Stop, Think, and Pray

Look over the "Ask Yourself" questions. How is God speaking to you? How do you need to respond? Be specific about what you need to do, and when you're going to do it.

REMEMBER

One way to remember the truths you have studied is to choose key Bible verses and memorize them. You can select your own verses from the passages you study, or memorize the one suggested at the end of each lesson. (See page 89 for help in memorizing Scripture.)

Suggested memory verse about holiness

But just as he who called you is holy, so be holy in all you do; for it is written: "Be holy, because I am holy." (1 Peter 1:15-16)

NOTES: 1. A.W. Pink, as quoted in *Knowing God*, by J.I. Packer (Downers Grove, Illinois: InterVarsity Press, 1979), page 142.

2. A. W. Tozer, *The Knowledge of the Holy* (New York: Harper & Row Publishers, 1961), pages 77-78.

3. Jerry Bridges, *The Pursuit of Holiness* (Colorado Springs, Colorado: NavPress, 1978), page 85.

4. J.I. Packer, *I Want to Be a Christian* (Eastbourne, England: Kingsway Publications, 1977), page 163.

Faith

The Christian life begins with faith as we put our trust in Christ and His work on the cross. That initial act of faith is only the beginning, however. Being a Christian means committing ourselves to a totally new view of the world. God *is* there. Although we cannot see Him, He is the ultimate reality. We need to adjust all of life to reflect that reality. This is the life of faith. As expressed in Hebrews 11:1, "Faith is being sure of what we hope for and certain of what we do not see."

In this lesson we will see that the importance of faith cannot be overestimated. In particular, we will examine the life of Abraham, one of the more prominent people in the Old Testament. His life clearly illustrates the nature of faith, and will help us understand how we can grow in faith. If you are able to, make Genesis 11:27-25:11 (the record of Abraham's life) your reading program for the next few days. This will greatly enhance your study.

Pause for Prayer

Our attitude toward the Lord is reflected in our attitude toward His Word. God Himself said, "This is the one I esteem: he who is humble and contrite in spirit, and trembles at my word" (Isaiah 66:2). Ask God to give you this reverent and responsive attitude toward His Word as you do this lesson.

The Importance of Faith

Without faith it is impossible to please God.

(Hebrews 11:6)

---

1. Jesus spent much time preparing the twelve disciples for their future service. What do you think they learned about faith from the following incidents recorded in Mark's gospel?

   4:35-40

   6:7-9

   9:17-29

   11:12-14, 20-24

Jesus gave considerable attention to developing faith in His disciples. He taught them about its importance. He gave them experiences that demanded faith. On several occasions He strongly rebuked them for lack of faith. He drew attention to faith in others. Above all, He transmitted His own unshakable confidence in God.

2. Prayerfully consider Hebrews 11:6. What insight does this verse give into the importance of faith?

ASK YOURSELF: Why is it that without faith it is impossible for me to please God?

"I believe the need of the hour is for an army of soldiers dedicated to Jesus Christ with eyes single to His glory, who believe not only that He is God, but that He can fulfill every promise He has ever made." — DAWSON TROTMAN*

Abraham, Man of Faith

3. In the following passages from the Book of Genesis, what stands out to you about Abraham's faith? It may be a way

he expressed his faith in God. It may be a way in which he failed to trust God. Or it may be how he developed in faith. Don't limit yourself to one observation about each passage.

12:1-13

15:1-18

17:1-18

22:1-18

Additional references from Genesis: 13:5-18; 16:1-6; 20:1-18; 24:1-7

"O.K. Grog, don't try anything cute. Just circle the valley a couple of times and I'll meet you down at the cave."

4. What have you learned about God from the passages that record His dealings with Abraham?

"All God's giants have been weak men who did great things for God because they reckoned on God being with them."

— HUDSON TAYLOR*

ASK YOURSELF: How can Abraham's life serve as an example to me as I try to trust God?

(Abraham is one of many Old Testament examples of faith. Hebrews 11 gives a list of some others that can be studied the same way we have considered Abraham. Look up the person's name in a Bible concordance to find all the references for that person.)

Living by Faith
Romans 4:18-21 is an excellent passage for clarifying the nature of faith and giving insight into how we can grow in faith. Read it several times.

God's Word
So keep up your courage, men, for I have faith in God that it will happen just as he told me.
(Acts 27:25)

5. According to Romans 4:18 and 20, what prompted Abraham to believe?

6. Second Peter 1:3-8 is a good passage about the promises of God.

   a. How does Peter describe God's promises?

   b. How can they help us?

   c. What should our response be?

Claiming Promises

A promise of God is a commitment that He will do something, but we must first respond with faith. Sometimes that might mean patiently waiting for the Lord to do what He promises. Other times it may mean launching out into the unknown or taking a risk. Always, though, the focus must be on God and His glory.

There are two kinds of promises. General promises are clearly addressed to all believers and apply in any situation. We need to familiarize ourselves with these promises and act on them. Some examples are Matthew 6:33 and 18:20, John 15:7, 1 Corinthians 10:13 and 15:58, 2 Corinthians 9:6-7, and Philippians 4:6-7.

Specific promises were given to individuals in the Bible on specific occasions. It may be that the Holy Spirit will show you the relevance of such a promise for a situation you face. Be sure that you are interpreting the promise correctly and that the proposed application is valid. Particularly if you are a relatively new Christian, other believers with a greater knowledge of God's Word can help you. In addition, because of possible misuse, it is wise to allow time and prayer to confirm that this is a genuine promise and not just a subjective impression. Specific promises have stirred many people to great acts of faith.

God's Character

> *"Have faith in God," Jesus answered.*
> (Mark 11:22)

---

7. Romans 4:20-21 indicates that Abraham was able to endure difficult circumstances in faith. What was the foundation of his faith?

8. Abraham illustrates a general principle that is found in Psalm 9:10. Write this principle in your own words.

Faith does not focus on itself. Its function is to link us with the powerful and faithful God. If we are worrying whether or not we have the right quantity or quality of faith, we have missed the point. The greatness or smallness of our faith is not crucial, but our willingness to trust a great God is.

"Expect great things from God. Attempt great things for God."
— WILLIAM CAREY*

ASK YOURSELF: What can I do to deepen my faith in God?

For Further Study

Our appreciation of God's power and goodness is the foundation of our faith. Therefore, by meditating on the character of God as revealed in the Bible, our faith can be strengthened.

Read Job 26, Isaiah 40, or Jeremiah 32. Then ask yourself, What does it teach about God's goodness and power? How can I adjust my life to this truth?

God Alone

We live by faith, not by sight.
(2 Corinthians 5:7)

---

9. a. What truth about God is illustrated in Romans 4:19-20?

   b. According to Romans 4:17, why is it reasonable to
      expect the seemingly impossible?

---

10. How do the following verses stress God's unlimited power?

    Proverbs 3:5-6

    Jeremiah 17:5-8

"[Faith] is strengthened by the removal of human props. It increases through response to the requirements and challenges of His Word. Contrary to popular belief, it is not always fostered by great encouragements and swift answers to prayer. It thrives more in the midst of difficulties and conflicts when all secondary support has been removed."[1] —J. OSWALD SANDERS

ASK YOURSELF: In what way can I step out in faith, depending on God to work in a situation that appears unpromising?

Stop, Think, and Pray

Look over the "Ask Yourself" questions in the lesson. How is God speaking to you about faith? Perhaps you have been challenged in a number of areas. Ask God to help you select the one that is most important now. What is He asking you to do?

The most important lesson

My response

Suggested memory verse about faith

Yet he did not waver through unbelief regarding the promise of God, but was strengthened in his faith and gave glory to God, being fully persuaded that God had power to do what he had promised. (Romans 4:20-21)

NOTES: 1. J. Oswald Sanders, *Mighty Faith* (Sevenoaks, England: Overseas Missionary Fellowship, 1964), page 22.

Wisdom

How often have you wondered what to do when faced with a decision? Some people act on impulse. Some don't act at all, preferring to let circumstances dictate. Others seem to have the knack for making good decisions. The Bible calls this wisdom. It is not the same as cleverness; clever people can make a real mess of their lives. Wisdom is moral clear-sightedness—the ability to know what is right and then to do it.

What gives a person such insight? Are some people just born wise? The Bible indicates that wisdom is available for all God's people. In this lesson we will examine how to become wise and how to apply wisdom in daily life.

Pause for Prayer

Proverbs 4:7 tells us, "Wisdom is supreme; therefore get wisdom. Though it cost all you have, get understanding." Ask God to help you pay the price in effort.

The Wisdom of God

Oh, the depth of the riches
of the wisdom and knowledge of God!
How unsearchable his judgments,
and his paths beyond tracing out!
(Romans 11:33)

1. Read Job 28:1-28. What is the difference between man's natural knowledge and biblical wisdom?

The Book of Job is known as wisdom literature, a style of writing that was common in the ancient Near East. It is found in the Old Testament, mainly in Job, a few psalms, Proverbs, and Ecclesiastes. In his book, Job grapples with the problem of suffering. After much debate between Job and his friends, God speaks (Job 38:1-42:6). If you have time, read all five chapters.

2. Read Job 38:1-4, 40:1-14, and 42:1-6.

   a. What is the Lord's criticism of Job?

   b. What conclusion does Job come to?

3. According to Proverbs 3:5-6 and 9:10, what is the source of wisdom?

"Conviction of ignorance is the doorstep to the temple of wisdom." — C.H. SPURGEON*

ASK YOURSELF: Job was guilty of darkening God's counsel "with words without knowledge" (Job 38:2). Are there any situations in which I am tempted to think that I know better than God?

The Nature of Wisdom

Who is wise and understanding among you?
Let him show it by his good life,
by deeds done in the humility
that comes from wisdom.
(James 3:13)

---

4. Like the Book of Job, Proverbs is wisdom literature. The first seven verses form a general introduction to the book. Meditate on these verses, using the questions listed below. Then write a definition of wisdom.

- What other words are used here to describe wisdom?
- What is the purpose of wisdom?
- What is the source of wisdom?
- Who can receive wisdom and who cannot?

My definition

5. Think about Deuteronomy 29:29. What can it teach us about the kind of wisdom God wants us to have?

"God in His wisdom, to make and keep us humble and to teach us to walk by faith, has hidden from us almost everything that we should like to know about the providential purposes which He is working out in the churches and in our own lives. . . . [Wisdom] is not a sharing in all His knowledge, but a disposition to confess that He is wise, and to cleave to Him and live for Him in the light of His Word through thick and thin."[1] —J.I. PACKER

6. According to James 3:13-17, what characterizes true wisdom?

ASK YOURSELF: How can I tell whether I am growing in godly wisdom, or just increasing my knowledge?

The Gift of Wisdom

For the LORD gives wisdom, and from his mouth
come knowledge and understanding.
(Proverbs 2:6)

---

7. The Book of Proverbs is a collection of the sayings of
   Solomon. According to 1 Kings 4:29, "God gave Solomon
   wisdom and very great insight, and a breadth of understanding as measureless as the sand on the seashore." Read.
   1 Kings 3:5-15 to find out what prompted God's gift.

---

8. Read James 1:5-8 Then change the wording so that instead
   of being a general promise, it is a specific promise for you.

---

9. The primary way in which God reveals His wisdom to us is
   through the Bible: "The holy Scriptures . . . are able to
   make you wise" (2 Timothy 3:15). Read Proverbs 2:1-6 and
   write down the attitudes and actions that will help us gain
   that wisdom.

"The Word of God is like a great treasure house of spiritual truth. The door is fastened by a number of locks that guard its precious truths from the halfhearted and from those who are merely curious but have no real spiritual hunger or intent to apply its words to their hearts."[2] — LEROY EIMS

ASK YOURSELF: Is there a current situation in which I need wisdom? How seriously am I praying about it and searching the Bible for answers?

Wisdom and Daily Life

Be very careful, then, how you live—
not as unwise but as wise,
making the most of every opportunity,
because the days are evil.
(Ephesians 5:15-16)

10. The New Testament draws attention to our need for wisdom in order to make the most of life. Using the following references in Colossians, list areas of life in which wisdom can help us.

1:9-10

1:28

3:16

11. Read Proverbs 6:6-8 and 24:30-34. What source of wisdom do the passages point to? Also read Proverbs 1:20.

"The activity of acquiring new skills, developing new attitudes, formulating new relationships, discovering, daring, exploring, reforming, renewing—in short, learning—is what makes life the adventure Jesus promised." —WALDRON SCOTT

We need to distinguish between having experience and learning from experience. We gain wisdom only as we reflect upon experience and test our conclusions against the Bible. If we are willing to do that, the whole of life can be a learning experience.

12. The first nine chapters of Proverbs are an introduction to the nature and value of wisdom. The rest of the book consists of hundreds of statements that give a wealth of insight into daily living. Choose one of the three topics listed below, look up the verses, and write down what you learn.

Humility	Relationships	Speech
11:2	12:16	10:19
12:15	13:15	10:21

Humility	Relationships	Speech
13:10	14:22	11:13
16:5	16:7	12:18
16:18	17:9	12:22
16:19	18:1	12:25
18:12	22:24-25	15:1
26:12	25:17	15:23
27:2	27:6	27:14
27:21	27:9	29:20

ASK YOURSELF: What am I learning these days that is helping me live a more godly life?

For Further Study

The contrast between God's wisdom and man's cleverness is an important theme of the Bible. It is particularly brought out in 1 Corinthians 1:17-2:16.

A. What does this passage reveal about the limitations of human wisdom?

B. How did God make known His secret wisdom?

C. Who is able to receive God's wisdom?

D. How should these truths affect our attitude?

Stop, Think, and Pray

Jesus said, "Everyone who hears these words of mine *and puts them into practice* is like a *wise* man who built his house on the rock" (Matthew 7:24, italics added). What have you heard God saying to you through this lesson? You may find it helpful to look over the "Ask Yourself" questions again. Ask God to help you make wise plans to put into practice what He has taught you.

How God spoke to me

My plan to put this into practice

Suggested memory verse about wisdom

If any of you lacks wisdom, he should ask God, who gives generously to all without finding fault, and it will be given to him. (James 1:5)

NOTES: 1. J.I. Packer, *Knowing God* (Downers Grove, Illinois: InterVarsity Press, 1973), pages 96-97.
2. LeRoy Eims, *Wisdom from Above* (Wheaton, Illinois: Victor Books/ Scripture Press, 1978), page 39.

Prayer

"The one concern of the devil is to keep Christians from praying. He fears nothing from prayerless studies, prayerless work, prayerless religion. He laughs at our toil, mocks our wisdom, but trembles when we pray."[1] Samuel Chadwick's bold declaration is echoed throughout the history of the Christian Church.

This recognition of the importance of prayer finds its origin in the Bible; the principle is written on page after page. We will look first at the example of Jesus because He alone can inspire us to become people of prayer. We will also investigate some types of prayer.

This lesson is brief for such an important topic, but as we apply these truths about prayer, God can lead us on and teach us more. Praying is best learned in the doing!

Pause for Prayer

If you call out for insight
and cry aloud for understanding,
and if you look for it as for silver
and search for it as for hidden treasure,
then you will understand the fear of the LORD
and find the knowledge of God.
For the LORD gives wisdom,
and from his mouth come knowledge and understanding.

(Proverbs 2:3-6)

Pray that the attitude described in these verses will be true of you as you study God's Word.

The Example of Jesus

During the days of Jesus' life on earth,
he offered up prayers and petitions
with loud cries and tears.
(Hebrews 5:7)

The Centrality of Prayer

Apart from me you can do nothing.
(John 15:5)

---

1. The following passages in Luke describe some of the main events in Jesus' public ministry. What can you learn from them about the place of prayer in Jesus' daily life?

   3:21-22

   6:12-13

   9:18-20

   9:28-29

22:31-32

22:39-46

---

2. Read Luke 11:1 and Acts 6:2-4. How did spending time with Jesus affect the disciples' attitude toward prayer?

===

"We automatically place first that which we deem most important. If prayer is meager, it is because we consider it supplemental, not fundamental. To our Lord it was not a reluctant addendum, but a fundamental necessity."[2] —J. OSWALD SANDERS

===

ASK YOURSELF: If I consider prayer to be of first importance, how should this show itself in my life?

The Discipline of Prayer

Go into your room, close the door and pray.
(Matthew 6:6)

---

3. What do the following passages teach about Jesus' attitude toward prayer?

Matthew 14:22-23

Mark 1:32-35

Luke 5:15-16

---

4. **a.** Meditate on Matthew 6:6. What does it teach about personal prayer?

b. How is the application of Matthew 6:6 illustrated in the following references?

Psalm 5:1-3

Daniel 6:10

"One sometimes hears it said, 'I confess that I do not spend much time in the secret chamber, but I try to cultivate the habit of continual prayer.' And it is implied that this is more and better than that. The two things ought not to be set in opposition. Each is necessary to a well-ordered Christian life; and each was perfectly maintained in the practice of the Lord Jesus."[3]

— D.M. McINTYRE

ASK YOURSELF: How can I apply greater discipline so that my prayer life will be strengthened?

The Spirit of Prayer

The Spirit helps us in our weakness.
(Romans 8:26)

As we observe Jesus' prayer life and try to follow His example and teaching, we realize our inadequacies. Prayer is hard work. Prayer is humbling. Prayer involves searching for the will of God. Prayer is warfare because it is vigorously opposed by Satan. Here, perhaps more than in any area of Christian living, we know that we could not succeed if left to ourselves.

5. Look at Galatians 4:6.

   a. How does the Spirit transform our approach to God?

b. The Holy Spirit is referred to here as "the Spirit of his Son." Think about all that you have just read about Jesus' prayer life. How do you react to the realization that the Spirit of Jesus is in you?

---

6. Consider Ephesians 6:18.

a. What involvement should the Spirit have in our praying?

b. What is our part in allowing the Spirit to fulfill His ministry? Also refer to Romans 8:5.

c. What should be our attitude toward prayer?

"Dear God, I know Your Word says You even know the number of hairs on my head, but in case You've lost track, it's down to 216."

d. What reassurance can you find in Romans 8:26-27?

"In prayer it is better to have a heart without words, than words without a heart." —JOHN BUNYAN*

ASK YOURSELF: In what ways do I particularly need the Holy Spirit to direct and help me in my praying?

All Kinds of Prayers

Pray in the Spirit on all occasions
with all kinds of prayers and requests.
(Ephesians 6:18)

---

7. What kinds of prayer can you discover in the following verses?

Nehemiah 9:1-3

Psalm 100

Ephesians 6:18-20

1 Timothy 2:1-2

Praise

How good it is to sing praises to our God,
how pleasant and fitting to praise him.
(Psalm 147:1)

---

8. Read Psalm 103:1-5.

a. How does David get himself into a praising frame of mind?

b. Write down some "benefits" you have received from God.

Thanksgiving and praise are closely linked. A wife may thank her husband for going to the grocery store. That is thanksgiving. It may lead, however, to expressions of personal appreciation: "I am so glad I married you. You're very helpful." That is praise.

In the same way, we can go from thanking God to adoring Him for who He is. This is particularly true as we thank Him for our salvation in Christ, because His work of salvation reveals His character with special clarity.

---

9. Focus on Psalm 145:1-7.

a. What decision does David make?

b. Why does he want to praise God?

c. Verses 3-21 list numerous characteristics of God for which David wants to praise Him. Choose one characteristic that you are particularly excited about, perhaps one you have become aware of in a new way recently. (It need not be listed in the psalm.) Write a brief paragraph expressing your praise to God.

> "We should pray when we are in a praying mood, for it would be sinful to neglect so fair an opportunity. We should pray when we are not in a praying mood, for it would be dangerous to remain in so unhealthy a condition." — CHARLES H. SPURGEON*

When we are in a praising mood, the psalms can often put into words what we feel but find hard to express. When we are not in a praising mood, the thoughts and emotions of the psalmist can often lift us up.

Praising God with other Christians is a great help. In this lesson, we are focusing on private worship, but the discipline of regular group worship should stimulate our personal prayer life.

ASK YOURSELF: How can I improve my private worship of God?

Confession

> *If I had cherished sin in my heart,*
> *the Lord would not have listened.*
> (Psalm 66:18)

Confession of sin is our first act when we become Christians. But even after having found our acceptance through Christ, there will still be many times when confession is necessary.

---

10. Read 1 John 1:5-9.

a. What does the phrase *walk in the light* convey to you?

b. What is a vital part of walking in the light?

c. Look at the example of David in the verses below. What can you learn about walking in the light?

Psalm 119:59-60

Psalm 139:23-24

d. What reassurance do you get from the passage?

The root meaning of the word *confess* is "to agree." Instead of trying to justify ourselves, we agree with God's evaluation that our action or attitude is sin.

11. We can at any moment recognize sin, confess it, and claim forgiveness through the blood of Christ. Nevertheless, there is a place for more deliberate, worshipful confession. Psalm 51 is a good illustration of this.

a. What is David's attitude toward his sin?

b. How does he think it affects his life?

c. What does he ask God to do for him?

"Think of the *guilt of sin*, that you may be humbled. Think of the *power of sin*, that you may seek strength against it. Think not of the *matter of sin* . . . lest you be more and more entangled."
—JOHN OWEN*

Requests

*Morning by morning I lay my requests before you
and wait in expectation.*
(Psalm 5:3)

This final section focuses on Matthew 21:22. Begin by reading the context (verses 18-22).

---

12. *"If you believe"*

    a. What can help you believe?

       2 Corinthians 1:20

       James 5:17-18

    b. According to Luke 18:1-8, how should faith affect your praying?

As we make specific requests, we can watch expectantly for God to answer. As He does, and we thank Him, our faith will grow and our requests will get bigger.

13. *"You will receive"*

    a. In Matthew 7:7-11, what truth about God does Jesus impress on His disciples?

    b. According to John 16:24, what is the effect of receiving answers to prayer?

14. *"Whatever you ask for in prayer"*

    a. How does 1 John 5:14-15 qualify this idea?

    b. What guidance is provided in the following verses to help us pray as we should?

    Matthew 18:19-20

    John 14:13

John 15:7

James 4:3

ASK YOURSELF: What am I currently asking God to do?

For Further Study
Jesus gave His disciples a pattern for prayer in Matthew 6:9-13. Meditate on His prayer phrase by phrase.

A. What does it teach about our approach to God?

B. What does it teach about priorities in praying?

C. How can you use these words as a framework for prayer?

Stop, Think, and Pray

As you reflect on what you have learned about prayer in this lesson, how do you think God is leading you to respond? For an activity like prayer, it is easy to make ambitious plans that soon fall flat. Ask God to help you make a realistic plan.

REMEMBER

Suggested memory verse about prayer

> **Do not be anxious about anything, but in every-thing, by prayer and petition, with thanksgiving, present your requests to God. (Philippians 4:6)**

NOTES: 1. Samuel Chadwick, as quoted in *Master Secrets of Prayer*, by Cameron V. Thompson (Lincoln, Nebraska: Back to the Bible, 1979), page 9.
2. J. Oswald Sanders, *Effective Prayer* (Sevenoaks: Overseas Missionary Fellowship, 1961), page 6.
3. D.M. McIntyre, *The Hidden Life of Prayer* (Minneapolis: Bethany Fellowship, Inc., n.d.), page 33.
4. Sanders, *Effective Prayer*, page 11.

Serving

Jesus' teaching continually challenged contemporary values. Nowhere is this more apparent than in what He had to say about greatness. The leaders of His day measured greatness by how much authority they had to command obedient and respectful service. Jesus turned that concept upside-down. He taught that true greatness is the willingness to give humble and sacrificial service. As with all of Jesus' teaching, His life illustrated the truth.

In this lesson, we will consider Jesus' lifestyle of serving. We will see how He sought to instill the willingness to serve in His disciples.

Living for others is not natural to us in our fallen state, but the Spirit of Christ can renew us in this area as in all others. We will investigate the necessary attitudes and how to develop them with the Spirit's help.

Pause for Prayer

In the last lesson, we were reminded that prayer is indispensable. Jesus said, "Apart from me you can do nothing" (John 15:5). That certainly includes Bible study, so take time now to seek God's help as you consider the questions. Jesus' promise is that such dependence on Him yields much fruit.

The Way of Jesus

Jesus' Lifestyle

I am among you as one who serves.
(Luke 22:27)

---

1. Read the following incidents recorded in Mark's gospel. What can you learn from each one about Jesus' commitment to serving people?

    1:32-42

    2:13-17

    4:33-34

    6:30-46

Additional references in Mark: 3:1-6; 3:20; 10:13-16

---

2. What impresses you about the incident recorded in John 19:25-27?

The word *ministry*, another word for service, is used to describe Jesus' public life. His whole life was consumed with serving.

Jesus' Teaching

Whoever wants to be first must be slave of all.
(Mark 10:44)

---

3. Jesus used life situations to teach His disciples the importance of humble service. Read about two such incidents in Mark's gospel. What can you learn about the lifestyle Jesus wants His disciples to have?

   9:33-35

   10:35-45

---

4. Read Luke 17:7-10.

   a. How do you feel about what was expected of the servant?

b. What is the relevance of this illustration for you?

"[Jesus] was not laying down general principles of master-servant relationships. He was taking an illustration from contemporary life and using it to describe relationships in His Kingdom. The Messiah never intended men to glory in their own achievements. He wanted men who were more aware of their own unworthiness; men content to put duty before personal convenience."[1]

— DONALD GUTHRIE

An Unforgettable Lesson

Lord, are you going to wash my feet?
(John 13:6)

On the eve of His death, Jesus took the opportunity to impress on His disciples the importance of serving. It is an unforgettable lesson, recorded for us in John 13:1-17. Read this passage and then consider the questions below. (The normal practice was to wash the feet of a guest when he arrived. The task was regarded as very menial and was usually relegated to the lowest slave. Guests at a meal reclined on couches arranged on three sides of a square. The two main guests sat on either side of the host.)

---

5. Focus on John 13:1-5.

   a. Why do you think one of the disciples didn't wash the guests' feet?

b. What was Jesus' attitude?

c. How do you think the disciples felt as Jesus washed their feet?

The conversation between Peter and Jesus in verses 6-11 indicates that there is more to Jesus' actions than just a lesson in humble service. He is giving them a picture of the Cross. Jesus' death was to be the culmination of His service, and would provide that deeper cleansing to which He alludes.

6. Read John 13:12-17.

a. How did Jesus emphasize the lesson to be learned from His action?

b. What do you think it means in today's world to wash one another's feet?

> "We would gladly wash the feet of our Divine Lord; but He disconcertingly insists on washing ours, and bids us wash our neighbor's feet." — WILLIAM TEMPLE*

   c. Read Matthew 25:40 and Colossians 3:23-24. How should these verses affect your willingness to obey Jesus' command to serve others?

> **ASK YOURSELF: a.** What is most likely to stop me from accepting the role of a servant? **b.** How can the truths studied in questions 1-5 motivate me to serve?

The Serving Lifestyle

A Servant's Attitude

> Your attitude should be the same
> as that of Christ Jesus.
> (Philippians 2:5)

We have observed the revolutionary way in which Jesus served others in His daily life. His actions reflect an underlying attitude. Philippians 2:3-11 gives remarkable insight into the way Jesus chose to be a servant.

---

7. Read the challenge in Philippians 2:3-4.

   a. What can hinder us from developing a servant's attitude?

b. What should be our attitude toward others? (Read the illustration in Philippians 2:19-22.)

It is important to distinguish between true and false humility. True servants do not apologize for their existence! They are aware of their strengths and abilities and use them for the good of others. False humility engenders self-consciousness or self-hatred. These attitudes are as self-centered as self-assertion or self-will.

True servants can serve without being preoccupied with themselves or their performance. The focus of their thoughts and actions is the person in need. They are also free to allow themselves to *be served* when the occasion demands.

---

8. Now think about the example of Jesus in Philippians 2:5-8.

a. What voluntary decisions did Jesus make concerning His life?

b. What did these decisions cost Him?

c. Why do you think He made these choices?

> "Submission is an act of the will which must be repeated every time an opportunity to serve appears."[2] — RAY HOO

9. What does Philippians 2:9-11 teach us about God's attitude toward serving?

> **ASK YOURSELF:** In what ways can my attitude about serving be more Christlike?

A Servant's Actions

> *Now that you know these things,*
> *you will be blessed if you do them.*
> (John 13:17)

In this final section we will study 1 John 3:16-18, in which John summarizes what it takes to be an active servant.

10. a. What is the first step in serving others?

b. How can the principles in the following verses help us take the first step?

Matthew 7:12

2 Corinthians 8:16

Hebrews 10:24

---

11. a. What is the next step, according to 1 John 3:17-18?

b. How do the following passages illustrate this principle?

Acts 11:27-30

1 Corinthians 9:19-23

c. What point does Paul make in 2 Corinthians 8:11-12
about the link between motives, actions, and resources?

A servant learns to see and do, not see and say! Get in the habit of taking responsibility. And be aware that the major barriers are lack of love, pride, and laziness.

---

12. a. Read John 12:23-26 and 1 John 3:16. What kind of service should we give?

b. How would you define what this means?

"Self-denial is more than some slight insignificant reduction of our self-indulgence." — HUDSON TAYLOR*

ASK YOURSELF: What steps can I take to be a more active servant?

For Further Study
Four passages in Isaiah—42:1-4, 49:1-6, 50:4-7, and 52:13-53:12—are known as the "servant songs." They give a profile of the ideal servant of the Lord. As such, they portray Jesus Christ.

A. What are those things about Jesus' service for which you can praise God?

B. What insights into the attitudes and actions of a true servant do you find that will help you become Christlike?

"Teach us, good Lord, to serve Thee
as Thou deservest;
to give and not to count the cost;
to fight and not to heed the wounds;
to toil and not to ask for rest;
to labor and not to ask for any reward,
save that of knowing that we do Thy will."
— IGNATIUS*

Stop, Think, and Pray

As Christians, our goal is to become like the Lord Jesus Christ in character. In this lesson we have focused on Jesus' lifestyle of serving others. How did God speak to you about your own serving? Look back over the "Ask Yourself" questions. Then set a goal—a realistic, specific change in attitude toward serving. Prayerfully think of various activities that might help you reach that goal. Plan a time to review your progress.

Suggested memory verse about serving

Do nothing out of selfish ambition or vain conceit, but in humility consider others better than yourselves. Each of you should look not only to your own interests, but also to the interests of others. (Philippians 2:3-4)

NOTES: 1. Donald Guthrie, *Jesus the Messiah* (Grand Rapids, Michigan: Zondervan Publishing House, 1972), page 221.
2. Ray Hoo, *Called to Serve* (Colorado Springs, Colorado: NavPress, 1976), pages 24-25.

Suffering

Suffering is one of the harsh realities of life. For some, it means living with poor health. Others cope with difficult circumstances. As Christians, we are not immune from these normal human experiences of pain, sorrow, and hardship. What is more, by becoming Christians we open ourselves up to additional suffering. If we identify with Christ in a generally godless society, we can expect opposition. And if we genuinely care for our neighbors, we can expect heartache.

Must we just grin and bear it? Or is there a distinctively Christian attitude toward suffering? Where is God in the process? In this lesson we will search the Bible for answers.

Pause for Prayer

> *As the eyes of slaves*
> *look to the hand of their master,*
> *as the eyes of a maid*
> *look to the hand of her mistress,*
> *so our eyes look to the LORD our God.*
> (Psalm 123:2)

In the last lesson, we examined the qualities of a servant. As you begin this lesson, ask God to give you a servant's attentiveness to His Word.

Suffering in a Fallen World

We know that the whole creation has been groaning as in the pains of childbirth right up to the present time. Not only so, but we ourselves, who have the firstfruits of the Spirit, groan inwardly as we wait eagerly for our adoption as sons, the redemption of our bodies.

(Romans 8:22-23)

The Bible makes it clear that the world is not all that God intends it to be. Man's rebellion against God, and his consequent failure to exercise his God-given authority over the rest of creation, have resulted in pain and disorder. In a very real sense, suffering is a result of sin.

But this is not to suggest that there is in general a direct link between disease and wrongdoing; the Book of Job repudiates such a simplistic outlook. However, individuals do, to varying degrees, suffer the consequences of their sinful state.

---

1. Before you being to grapple with the issue of present suffering, spend a few moments thinking about God's promise in Revelation 21:1-5. What can you learn about God's attitude toward suffering?

---

2. Jesus constantly responded in compassion to those who were suffering. What can you learn from His responses to questions about suffering?

   Luke 13:1-5

John 9:1-3

ASK YOURSELF: How would I answer someone who says that no Christian with faith will ever be ill?

"God whispers to us in our pleasures, speaks in our conscience, but shouts in our pains. It is His megaphone to rouse a deaf world." — C.S. LEWIS*

Sharing in Christ's Sufferings

*To this you were called, because Christ suffered for you,
leaving you an example,
that you should follow in his steps.*
(1 Peter 2:21)

In addition to the suffering that is the common lot of fallen humanity, Christians experience another kind of suffering. This is the pressure that comes from seeking to live godly lives in a world that is hostile to God. In this, Christians follow in the footsteps of Christ Himself.

3. Prayerfully consider the following verses. What do they teach about suffering in the life of Jesus?

   Hebrews 2:18

"A bit of bad news, sir. The Rolls Royce is in the shop so you'll have to take the Mercedes to the country club."

Hebrews 5:7-9

1 Peter 2:23-24

---

4. What place does suffering have in the normal Christian life?

John 16:33

Acts 14:21-22

1 Thessalonians 3:2-4

The three passages in question 4 include the Greek word *thlipsis*. It is translated as "trouble," "hardship," "trial," "anguish," "affliction," "tribulation," and "suffering." Literally, the word means "pressure": the pressure of an ungodly world against the Christian who dares to swim against the stream; the pressure of serving God in the midst of need and hostility.

The pressure may be experienced in many forms. For some, their Christian faith and lifestyle may bring violent opposition, ill-treatment, and official oppression. For others, the pressure may take the form of verbal abuse or discrimination. Christian service may bring danger and discouragement, hardship and misunderstanding. (See Mark 13:9-13, Luke 6:22-23, and 2 Corin-

81

thians 11:23-33.) All who are seeking to live for Christ will meet pressure in one form or another (see 2 Timothy 3:12).

---

5. What should those who are facing this kind of pressure remember?

Romans 5:1-5

Romans 8:35-39

1 Peter 4:12-14

The apostles' lives give eloquent testimony to the fact that suffering goes hand in hand with serving Christ. In fact, it is essential if the mission is to progress (see Colossians 1:24). Such suffering is not, however, reserved for apostles. It is a necessary part of genuine Christian living; it is a mark of discipleship and a pledge of future glory (see Philippians 1:27-30 and 1 Peter 5:8-10). Furthermore, as we suffer, so we can identify more fully with Christ and come to know Him more intimately.

ASK YOURSELF: a. In what ways have I suffered because I'm a Christian? b. What encouragement can I draw from the passages in questions 3-5?

> "A Christian is someone who shares the sufferings of God in the world." — DIETRICH BONHOEFFER*

Trusting in God's Control

The LORD reigns, let the earth be glad.
(Psalm 97:1)

6. The truth of God's ultimate control of a fallen world is illustrated throughout the Bible. The following Old Testament passages focus on this theme of God's sovereignty. Meditate on each one. You might like to read them in more than one translation.

Write down those phrases or verses that most help you understand and feel the reality of God's sovereign control.

Psalm 33:8-11

Psalm 115:2-3

Isaiah 14:24

Isaiah 45:5-7

Isaiah 46:9-10

Daniel 4:34-35

---

7. Reflect on Romans 8:28-30. Then express what verse 28
means to you.

God is in control; He is not a victim of evil circumstances. In His
wisdom, He is able to use evil for good purposes. Hence, we can
accept the many difficult circumstances of life—both the
common human suffering and the special pressure on us as
Christians—as allowed by God to make us into the people He
wants us to be.

ASK YOURSELF: Are there any circumstances in my life in
which I do not believe that God is in control?

Recognizing God's Purposes
*So then, those who suffer according to God's will
should commit themselves to their faithful Creator
and continue to do good.*
(1 Peter 4:19)

God's purposes for our individual lives are not always clear to
us, especially in the midst of suffering. It is far more important

to trust in God's wise and loving control than to try to understand specifically what He is doing in our lives. Nevertheless, various passages in the Bible help us understand in a general way how God uses suffering. An appreciation of God's purposes can help us face difficulties with the right attitude.

---

8. Read 2 Corinthians 1:3-11. How did God use troubles and pressures in the lives of the Apostle Paul and his companions?

---

9. Read about one way Paul suffered in 2 Corinthians 12:7-10.

   a. How did he react to it?

   b. What effect did it have in his life?

---

10. Turn to Hebrews 12:5-11.

   a. What is the purpose of hardship?

b. What attitude should we have toward our difficulties?

---

11. Finally, consider James 1:2-4.

a. How does this passage present difficulties?

b. How should we respond to them?

> **ASK YOURSELF:** In what way do I need to change my attitude toward a current hardship or difficulty?

For Further Study

The life of Joseph is a striking illustration of God's control over evil circumstances and the way in which He uses them for His purposes and the good of His people. You may find it helpful to make Joseph's life a reading project for a few days. His birth is recorded in Genesis 30:22-24. Joseph comes to the fore in chapter 37 and is the leading figure through the end of Genesis. (If you read nothing else, read Genesis 50:20!) As you read, look at how Joseph responded to his circumstances and how God used suffering to mature him. How can Joseph's life encourage you?

Stop, Think, and Pray

How has your understanding increased as a result of this lesson on suffering? Look over the "Ask Yourself" questions. How is God speaking to you about your attitudes? Does your perspective on suffering need to change? Ask God to impress on you the main thing you should remember from this lesson. Summarize it below.

REMEMBER

Suggested memory verse about suffering

And we know that in all things God works for the good of those who love him, who have been called according to his purpose. (Romans 8:28)

Memorizing Scripture

As You Start to Memorize a Verse

1. Read in your Bible the context of each verse you memorize.
2. Try to gain a clear understanding of what each verse actually means. (You may want to read the verse in other Bible translations or paraphrases to get a better grasp of the meaning.)
3. Read the verse several times thoughtfully, aloud or in a whisper. This will help you grasp the verse as a whole. Each time you read it, say the topic, reference, verse, and then the reference again.
4. Discuss the verse with God in prayer, and continue to seek His help for success in Scripture memory.

While You Are Memorizing a Verse

5. Work on saying the verse aloud as much as possible.
6. Learn the topic and reference first.
7. After learning the topic and reference, learn the first phrase of the verse. Once you have learned the topic, reference, and first phrase and have repeated them several times, continue adding more phrases, one at a time.
8. Think about how the verse applies to you and your daily circumstances.
9. Always include the topic and reference as part of the verse as you learn it and review it.

After You Have Memorized a Verse

10. Write the verse from memory and check your accuracy. This deepens the impression in your mind.
11. Review the verse immediately after learning it, and repeat it frequently in the next few days. This is crucial for getting the verse firmly fixed in your mind, because of how quickly we tend to forget what we have recently learned.
12. REVIEW! REVIEW! REVIEW! Repetition is the best way to engrave the verse on your memory.

Who's Who

Below, listed in alphabetical order, are brief biographical sketches of the figures from the history of the Church who are quoted in this book.

Bonhoeffer, Dietrich (1906-1945)
German Lutheran minister and author. A strong opponent of the Nazis, he was imprisoned in 1943 and hanged shortly before the end of the war.

Bunyan, John (1628-1688)
Became a Christian through his wife. In 1655 he joined the Baptist church and began to preach. In 1660 he was arrested for preaching and held in Bedford jail for 12½ years. While in prison, he wrote the famous allegory *Pilgrim's Progress*.

Carey, William (1761-1834)
A shoemaker who became "the father of modern missions." In 1792 he helped organize the English Baptist Missionary Society and went to India as one of its first missionaries. He worked on translating the Bible into thirty-six languages and dialects, and was a strong advocate of two principles: the equality of missionaries and local people, and self-sustaining missions.

Ignatius (died about 115)
Bishop of Antioch. He wrote seven letters on his way to mar-

tyrdom in Rome, which form important documents on the early Church.

Müller, George (1805-1898)
Born in Germany, he was converted in 1825 through a Moravian mission. In 1829, he moved to England and became a pastor with the Plymouth Brethren. Wanting to help poor children, he established orphanages that were supported by unsolicited gift income. At the age of 70, he and his wife went on a worldwide evangelistic tour lasting seventeen years.

Owen, John (1616-1683)
English Puritan who became a friend and chaplain to Oliver Cromwell. He wrote several important books.

Spurgeon, Charles (1834-1892)
Victorian Baptist renowned for his direct and powerful preaching. Before he was 20 years old, he became pastor of New Park Street Chapel in London and soon drew vast crowds. The 6000-seat Metropolitan Tabernacle was erected, and Spurgeon preached there for thirty years. He also founded a college for pastors and trained some nine hundred men before his death.

Taylor, Hudson (1832-1905)
English medical student who went to China as a missionary in 1854 and adopted Chinese dress and customs. He soon left his missionary society, and formed the China Inland Mission, which emphasized an attitude of faith and prayer in raising money, and the need for field staff to control the mission. At his death, there were 205 mission stations, with 849 missionaries and 125,000 Chinese Christians.

Temple, William (1881-1944)
Archbishop of Canterbury, particularly noted for his concern for Christian unity and a just society.

Trotman, Dawson (1906-1956)
His burden for world evangelism and vision for multiplying workers led him to found The Navigators, a missionary organization dedicated to those ends.

For Further Reading

1. Holiness
Bridges, Jerry, *The Pursuit of Holiness,* NavPress
Packer, J.I., *God's Words,* InterVarsity Press
Ryle, John C., *Holiness,* Baker Book House

2. Faith
Miller, Basil, *George Müller: Man of Faith,* Bethany House
    Publishers

3. Wisdom
Eims, LeRoy, *Wisdom from Above,* Victor Books/Scripture
    Press
Packer, J.I., *Knowing God,* InterVarsity Press

4. Prayer
Bridges, Jerry, *How to Get Results Through Prayer,* NavPress
    (booklet)
Eims, LeRoy, *Prayer: More Than Words,* NavPress
Hallesby, O., *Prayer,* Augsburg Publishing House
McIntyre, D.M., *The Hidden Life of Prayer,* Baker Book
    House
Myers, Warren and Ruth, *Pray: How to Be Effective in
    Prayer,* NavPress
Sanny, Lorne, *How to Spend a Day in Prayer,* NavPress
    (booklet)

Wallis, Arthur, *Pray in the Spirit,* Christian Literature Crusade

5. Serving
Hoo, Ray, *Called to Serve,* NavPress (booklet)
Fletcher, William, *The Second Greatest Commandment,*
    NavPress

6. Suffering
Lewis, C.S., *A Grief Observed,* Bantam Books
Lewis, C.S., *The Problem of Pain,* The MacMillan Company